Brando's Golf Gad

Sonoma Publishers

P. O. Box 6779, Santa Rosa CA 95406 (707-566-9776)
www.sonomapublishers.com

Written by: Gary Brobst and Dan Frazier

Illustrations by: Dan Frazier, Shawn Lux, Steven Fontaine, Brianna Miller,

Trevor Gondola and Paul Kennemore

ISBN 0-9709468-1-3
First Printing
Printed in California, USA

Hey, don't forget Brando's first publication: "25 Ways to Cook Hot Dogs."

This book takes a light-hearted look at bachelors and the lives they lead. It presents 25 illustrated recipes that go along with those traditional bachelor lifestyles. There are some really cool gadgets in this book, too. Look for it at your local book or gift store.
ISBN 0-9709468-0-5

BRANDO'S GOLF GADGETS

Using Technology to Ace the Royal and Ancient Game

By Gary Brobst and Dan Frazier

Sonoma Publishers

Santa Rosa, CA

Dedication

Ah, GOLF - what a game it is - that royal and ancient game with its pasture land beginnings. The shepherds who invented the game never imagined it would succumb to graphite shafts, titanium "woods" and solid core balls. This book is dedicated to all you golfers out there who take the game seriously, who always want to score better, and who keep eyes focused for the newest golf gadgets!

Contents

My name is Brando and I rebuilt my first Chevy engine when I was 9. You might say that I am somewhat mechanically inclined... if you are the kind of person that regards the invention of the wheel a minor technological advance. When I graduated Summa Cum Grande With Cheese from a prestigious university, cosmology, genetic engineering, even nuclear technology companies were competing for my attention. As intriguing as these fields were, they just were not enough of a challenge for my intellect.

So I asked myself, what problem is worthy of my skills? What do people slave at for years with little or no improvement? What involves earth, wind, and water in deliberately diabolical combinations?

Golf!

Golf cries out for modern technological advancement. While inventing tools to shave strokes from the average golfer's game, I encountered resistance from traditional golf advocates. These dinosaurs insisted the new approach was cheating, merely because they had pared their scores down through the old dusty ritual called "practice." However, I have three avid golf buddies who have no problem pushing the envelope - of the rules, the equipment, and each other's tolerance. Over the years they have used my expertise to fill their golf bags with creative gadgets to conquer their most challenging holes. Here are their stories...

Chip *"Mr. Country Club"* Knurdson II

Chip B. Knurdson II is president and CEO of a large savings and loan. He holds a MBA degree from Yale with a specialization in "Legal Money Laundering." He has been married for 27 years (split up among four separate wives). His home on the 11th fairway of the Los Angeles Links is huge and cannot be hit by even the most errant drive. His winter home is on a course on Australia's Gold Coast. Chip got into golf through the endless business meetings circuit. After his initial exposure to the sport he found that he truly enjoyed this ancient pastime. It allowed him to buy and tote around expensive equipment as a status symbol, as well as wear shorts in a business setting. Money is no object with Chip, his game is as solid as thousand-dollar pro sessions and an eight hundred dollar driver can make it. But add a few of my patented Golf Gadgets, and he will be kicking corporate butt inside of one tax year!

Donald "*Lunch Bucket*" Donnelly

Donald is a young man of apparently flabby physique, but under that huge exterior is a considerable mass of sheer power. That, combined with his towering height of 6 feet 5 inches, makes him a formidable presence on the golf course. Donald started out playing football in high school and continued to play through college so his game-minded professors would pass him. It was only an act, however. The truth was that his heart had been stolen away by golf since his first game on the local links. After his first two balls powdered on impact, the third was driven through the retaining fence and into the window of a 1964 Impala a quarter of a mile away. Donald has been hooked on golf ever since.

Jake *"The Snake"* Greezman

Jake's been bouncing around the local golf links for years. I'm not even sure Jake has a regular job. He's always ready for a game, enticing unsuspecting golfers into bets they'd never make with friends. He'll bet on whether he wins the round, makes his current shot, that you don't make your shot, that people in the foursome ahead make or don't make their shots, and on the number of deer seen grazing on Hole 9. Greenies, sandies, birdies, and longest drives all ensure he can make payment on his double-wide "Love Pad" trailer. Natural deviousness has always been a major part of his golf game, and when it is combined with some Golf Gadgets, this man is unstoppable.

Hole #1

Long Shot

Long Shot
Par 4, 490 Yards

Key

Landing Area	
Sand Trap	
High Grass	
Heckler Zone	
Toxic Waste Site	
Out Of Bounds	

Tight Driving Lane

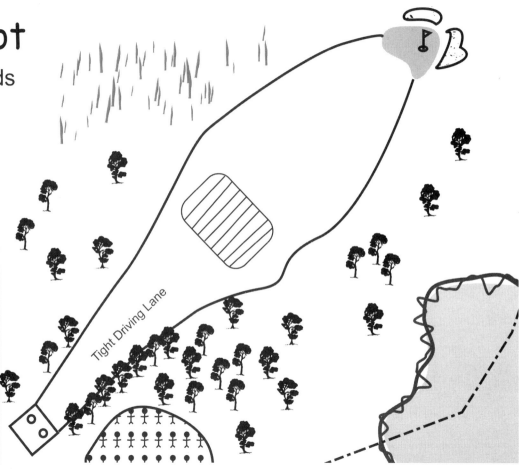

Look down that fairway! This is a par four on one of the local munis that's about two light years long. At 490 yards, it is longer than some real par fives. The wind is always blowing up your nose. Pars here are as rare as honest politicians. Bogies are not bad. If you dribble a shot, you may not get to the green in a normal life expectancy. Let's watch and see how Chip handles it.

Chip has to hit against major swirling winds.

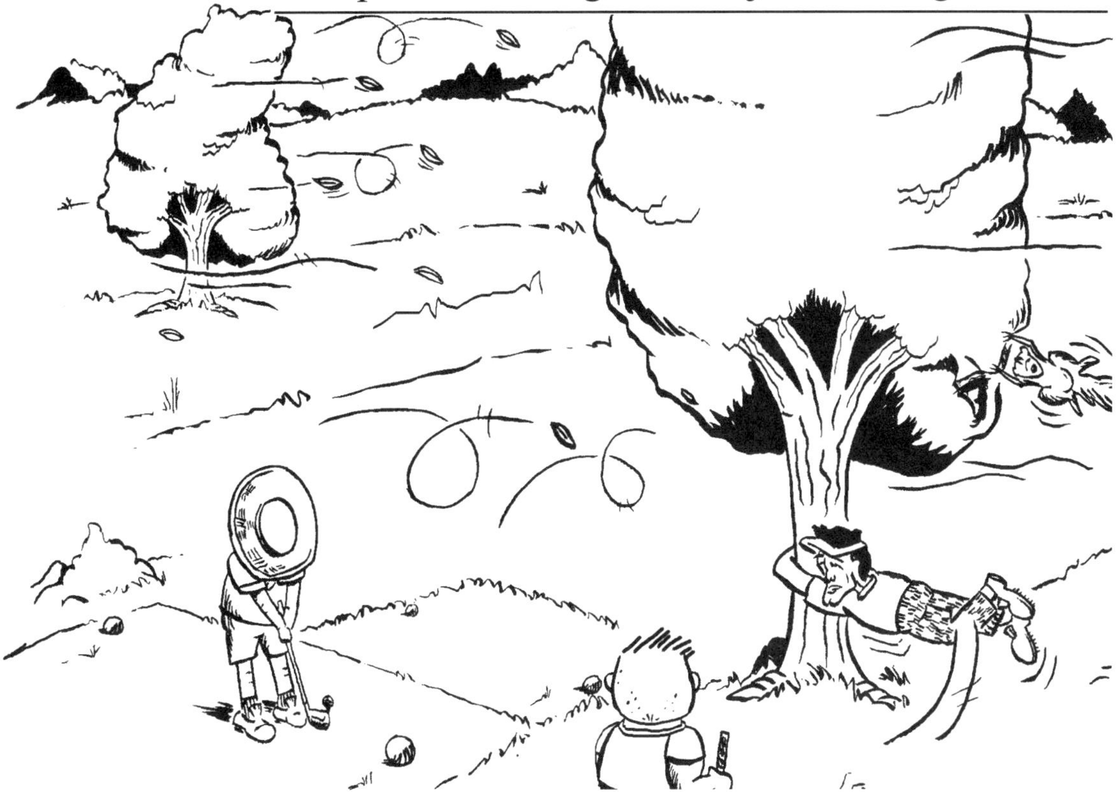

He chunks his first shot!

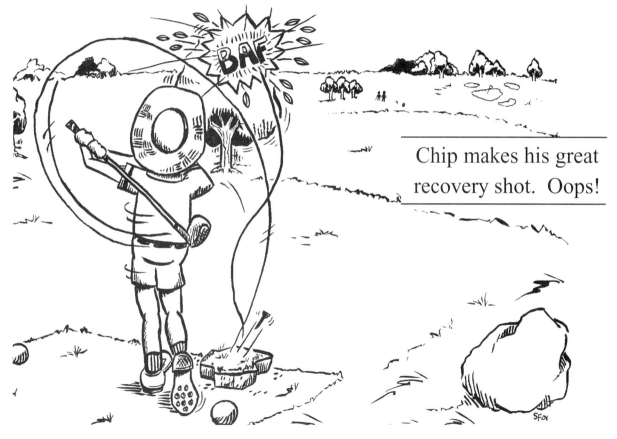

Chip makes his great recovery shot. Oops!

No shot here but a little punch out. Geez, now he lies three!

Brando's Golf Gadgets

While Donald and Jake wait patiently, Chip is back in the fairway, 350 yards away, hitting four. Not a snowball's chance of reaching the green, unless...

The Club Face Ball Launcher

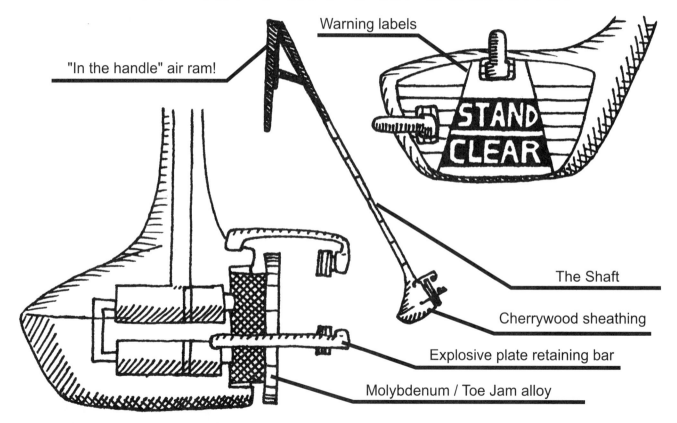

"In the handle" air ram!

Warning labels

STAND CLEAR

The Shaft

Cherrywood sheathing

Explosive plate retaining bar

Molybdenum / Toe Jam alloy

Chip really needs my help here. Luckily, his bag carries my Club Face Ball Launcher as the perfect club for extreme distances. The Ball Launcher uses compressed air to drive twin pneumatic rams behind the faceplate of the club. These rams are tripped when the club face meets the ball in excess of two miles per hour. The compressed air is generated by pumping the split-away portion of the handle repeatedly. The maximum pressure the club can achieve is 3000 lbs/square inch.

Chip's confidence increased after I introduced him to this club.

A few stealthy pumps of the handle; Chip blasts off a mighty 350 yarder!

Chip wins the hole! The Club Face Ball Launcher has met the challenge.

Alternate Uses for the Club Face Ball Launcher

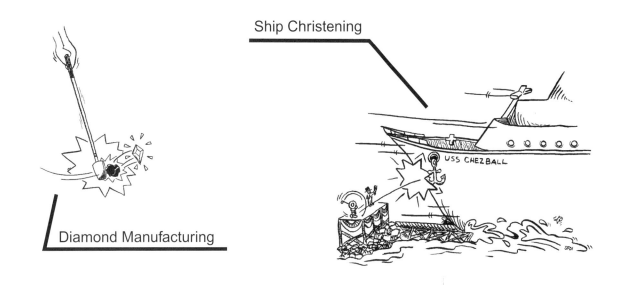

Ship Christening

USS CHEZBALL

Diamond Manufacturing

Hole #2

Rubber Ducky

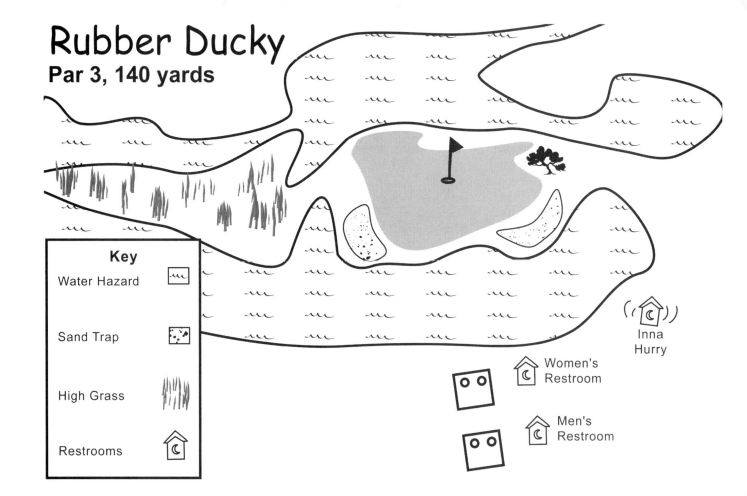

Rubber Ducky
Par 3, 140 yards

Key

Water Hazard

Sand Trap

High Grass

Restrooms

Inna
Hurry

Women's
Restroom

Men's
Restroom

Man the lifeboats! This hole on a river delta course has very little solid territory. Water to the left. Water to the right. Even water in front. Where there's no water, there is sand. Not a problem for most players, though, since it's only 140 yards long. But…you've gotta get there in the air or you will need a snorkel.

Poor Chip! Business and golf are a terrible combination.

Our man Chip is in big trouble this time. Now, normally Chip would simply drop another ball, take his penalty stroke, and try to salvage bogey. But wait! With a big dose of technology...and some divine intervention... there may be some hope for the Chipster.

The Moses Device

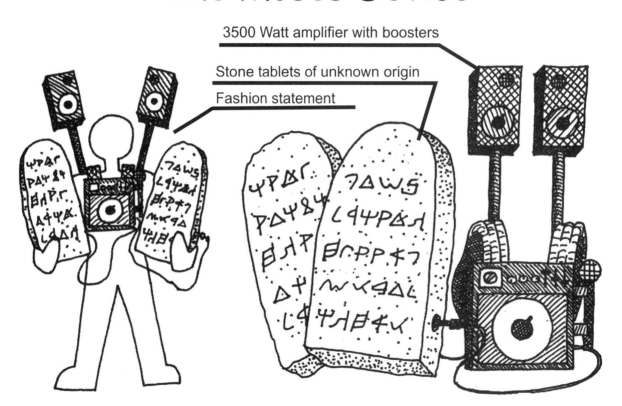

3500 Watt amplifier with boosters

Stone tablets of unknown origin

Fashion statement

The Moses Device is not strictly one of *my* inventions. One day as I was searching through an abandoned government warehouse looking for spare parts, I stumbled onto some ancient stone tablets in a corner. They were covered in dust and had some kind of scribbles chiseled all over them. This was so intriguing, I naturally took them home with me. After some intense experimentation, I discovered that they could channel the spirit of Moses! Wow! I thought, what could this do for my golf game? Hooking an 1100-watt amplifier and a distortion suppressor to the tablets improved the transmission, so when the PGA Tour was televised, I channeled the signal through. Moses was converted by the second round and became a great fan of the game.

Chip speed dials the Ancient One and Moses provides his support.

It's a miracle!

...and the caddy prepares the course for the next group.

Other uses for the Moses Device

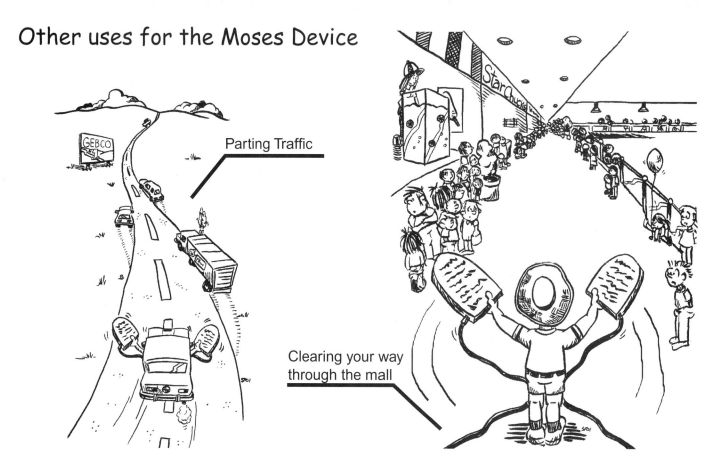

Parting Traffic

Clearing your way through the mall

Ever since Einstein introduced relativity, we have known that the speed of time itself can change. Using very sensitive instruments, I have measured the effects of playing golf on the temporal plane. The results may surprise you, but perhaps you have already noticed this yourself.

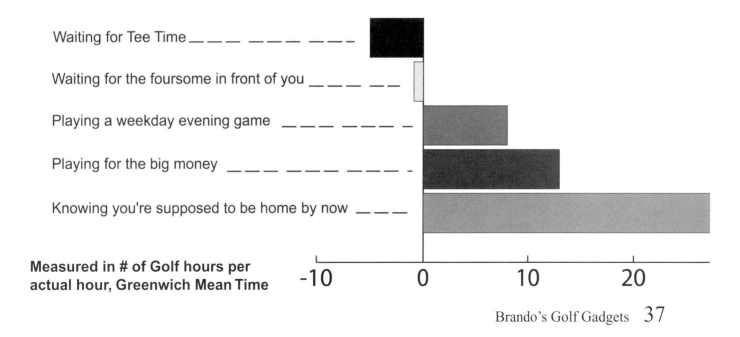

Waiting for Tee Time _ _ _ _ _ _ _ _ _

Waiting for the foursome in front of you _ _ _ _ _

Playing a weekday evening game _ _ _ _ _ _ _

Playing for the big money _ _ _ _ _ _ _ _ _ _

Knowing you're supposed to be home by now _ _ _

Measured in # of Golf hours per actual hour, Greenwich Mean Time

-10   0   10   20

Hole #3

The Big Sweat

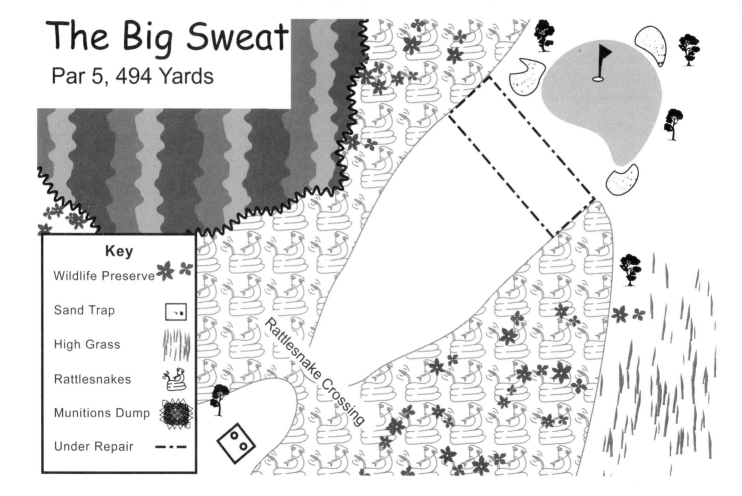

The Big Sweat
Par 5, 494 Yards

Key

Wildlife Preserve

Sand Trap

High Grass

Rattlesnakes

Munitions Dump

Under Repair

Rattlesnake Crossing

Ignore the desert all around you, and this is an easy hole. It's a straight away par 5 - just keep it in the fairway. Two decent shots and you've got a simple wedge to the green. It usually takes a birdie to win this hole.

Chip needs to birdie this hole. He's hecka down and this is a three hole carryover. There's a big bet on the line!

All 3 drives land in the fairway. Chip has visions of forking over some major assets to these bozos.

All second shots are nearly perfect. I told you this hole was easy.

All that's left is a simple wedge to the green. The hole looks enormous from here!

Jake knocks it right on the green with his third shot.

Donald is even closer!

Hoody Hoo! Chip bounces it off the flag stick! You da man!

Both his opponents two-putt for a par. Chip is so rattled that the hole appears to be shrinking.

The Putt-Puffer

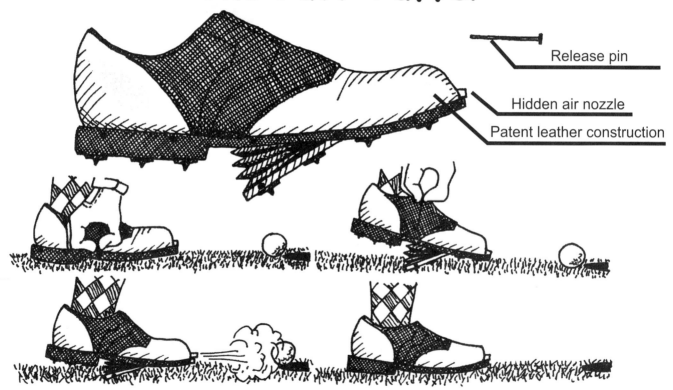

Release pin

Hidden air nozzle

Patent leather construction

Many putts come up 1 inch short. It is a scientific fact that over 99% of the putts that don't make it to the hole don't go in. The Putt-Puffer can make your ball the exception to that rule. Here's how it works:

The Putt-Puffer is a specially designed shoe implant with a bellows concealed in the sole. It provides a puff of air in a given direction when weight is applied. This is just enough to move one normal golf ball 2 inches on a wet green, with 3 days grass growth on Tuesdays (results on other days of the week may vary). This action is noiseless and invisible to the naked eye. The Putt-Puffer comes with a complete installation kit and fits into a man's shoe from size 6 to size 13. Men with shoe size over 13 should never come up short at any time! The Putt-Puffer will not fit or work in a woman's shoe. Women will mark this length putt anyway, carefully line it up, and putt it out successfully.

Alternate Uses for the Putt Puffer

Party balloon preparation

Camp fire starting

Bicycle tire repair

Hole #4

Back to Basics

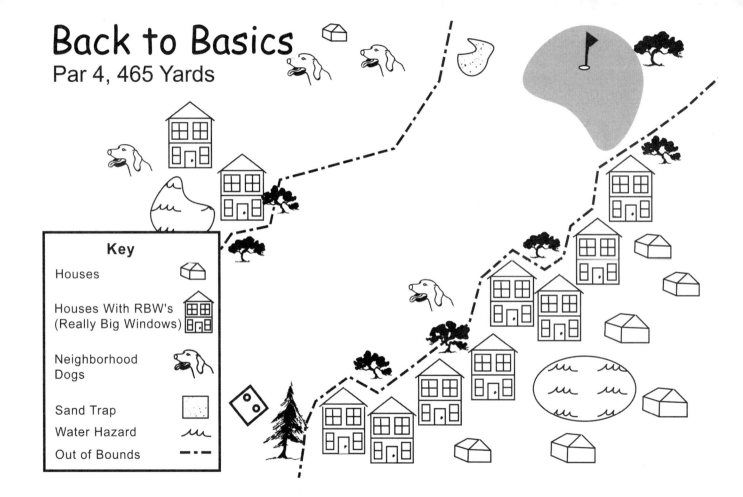

Back to Basics
Par 4, 465 Yards

Key

Houses

Houses With RBW's
(Really Big Windows)

Neighborhood
Dogs

Sand Trap

Water Hazard

Out of Bounds

This is a hole that Donald has trouble with from time to time (that is, from the last time to the next time). This is a long hole weaving through a residential community that Donald almost never reaches in four. Usually, he's happy just to get a double bogey! He definitely needs to shave some strokes here. Let's see if I can help him out with one of my Golf Gadgets.

Donald is nervous as he approaches the tee. Sure enough, he duffs his drive right into a bunker less than 80 yards ahead!

Donald's second stroke demonstrates his deft use of force. His precision is well known to club members... they're hiding inside the club house away from the windows.

There's still 350 yards to the pin. Donald draws his longest fairway wood, but he needs a bigger weapon.

Donald's ordinary woods are likely to snap under the swing force needed to reach the green. Expensive alloys and rare woods are all very well, but they are just too small and delicate for our friend here. With this hole in mind I went back to basic physics. A few simple calculations, and I discovered the prefect gadget for Donald!

The Basic Club

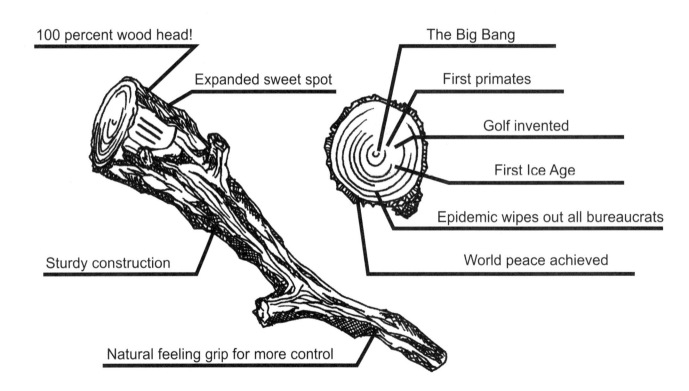

100 percent wood head!

Expanded sweet spot

The Big Bang

First primates

Golf invented

First Ice Age

Epidemic wipes out all bureaucrats

World peace achieved

Sturdy construction

Natural feeling grip for more control

Ah, The Basic Club; it has the simple beauty of a Shakespearean sonnet. Its clean lines are a breath of fresh air in the overly complex world of gadgetry. No titanium face, no graphite shaft - just the sheer power of heavy hardwood whistling through the atmosphere. Natural wood texture compliments the ability to crush a hapless golf ball for unbelievable distances. It is weather-resistant, inexpensive, and a self-contained theft deterent device. Truly, The Basic Club is one of my most brilliant inventions.

Donald and The Basic Club: love at first sight!

Donald carefully controls his form during this critical stroke.

How about that! A birdie on Donald's worst hole, and all thanks to The Basic Club. It solved this dilemma, but it's not the tool for every golfer. I have other gadgets that may be better for you.

Hole #5

Goesundagrass

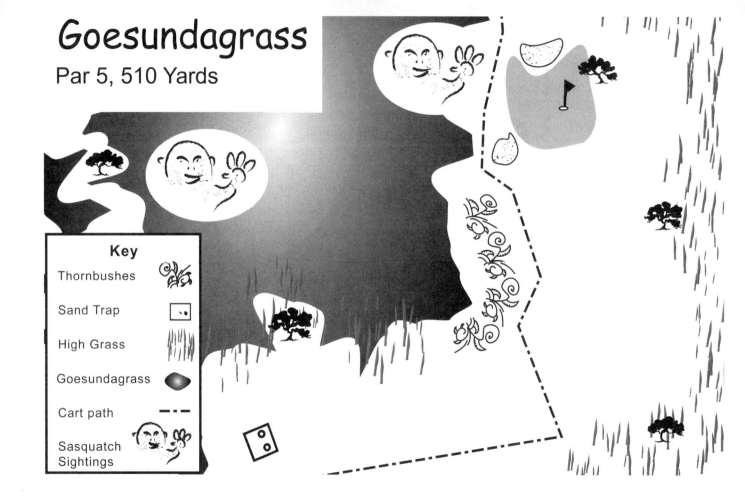

This is a tricky hole for our friend Donald. It's a reachable Par 5 on a wilderness course. The second shot requires accuracy to avoid the deadly Goesundagrass on the left. If your ball goes in da grass, it goes unda! Few have entered the area and lived to tell the tale, but rumor has it that somewhere in it lies the Ball Graveyard. Every ball in here has been scarred by cart paths, rocks or wedge blades. One thing's for sure - keep outa dat grass!

Donald steps to the tee for his first shot.
The drive is good, the wind slight…

Brando's Golf Gadgets

The ball misses the fairway but is not in any trouble yet. Donald is enjoying his commune with nature.

After sighting the green and lining it up, Donald selects a 3-wood. He unleashes, hoping to be on the green in two.

Disaster! Donald's ball heads straight for the Goesundagrass! Most people would abandon that ball, but Donald's not completely out of the hole yet. I have just the device for this jungle.

The BS3000 Brushwalker

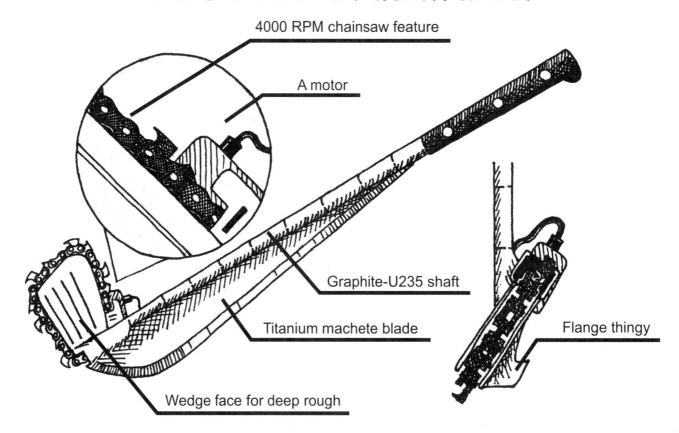

4000 RPM chainsaw feature

A motor

Graphite-U235 shaft

Titanium machete blade

Wedge face for deep rough

Flange thingy

Yes! The BS3000 Brushwalker, a marvel of negative engineering, is the next step for vegetatively challenged golfing. The 28-inch razor blade in the shaft is designed to make cutting through course jungles a snap! The hand closes firmly around the two-way handle in a comfortable power grip suitable for hacking and slashing. Once the ball is located, simply deploy the electric hedge trimmer attachment located on the underside of the club, and Voila! Instant fairway surface! I equipped the Brushwalker with a 60 degree wedge head so the ball would clear any surviving greenery on its way to the hole.

Nothing is sacred!
Donald's love affair
with nature is done.
Flora and fauna scatter
as his golf obsession
takes over.

Ah hah! He's found the ball hiding under a thick mat of Goesundagrass. The spreading branches of a couple of trees further complicate the shot...for the ordinary golf club!

Donald takes a few
practice strokes to be
sure he has a swing.

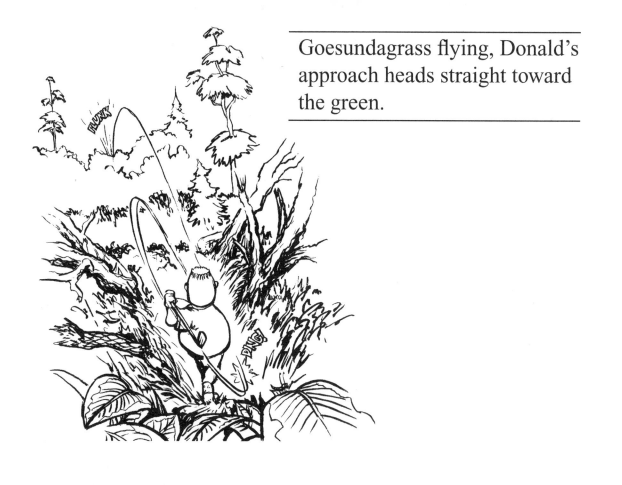

Goesundagrass flying, Donald's approach heads straight toward the green.

Alternate Uses for the
BS3000 Brushwalker

Yearly Expense Breakdown*

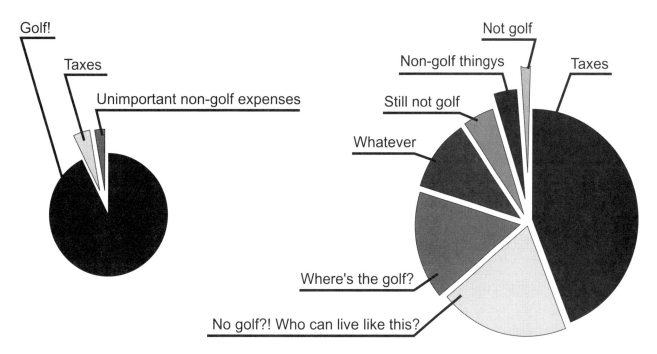

The Golfer

Golf!

Taxes

Unimportant non-golf expenses

The Non-Golfer

Not golf

Non-golf thingys

Still not golf

Whatever

Taxes

Where's the golf?

No golf?! Who can live like this?

*impartially adjusted for relative importance

Hole 6

Silence is Golden

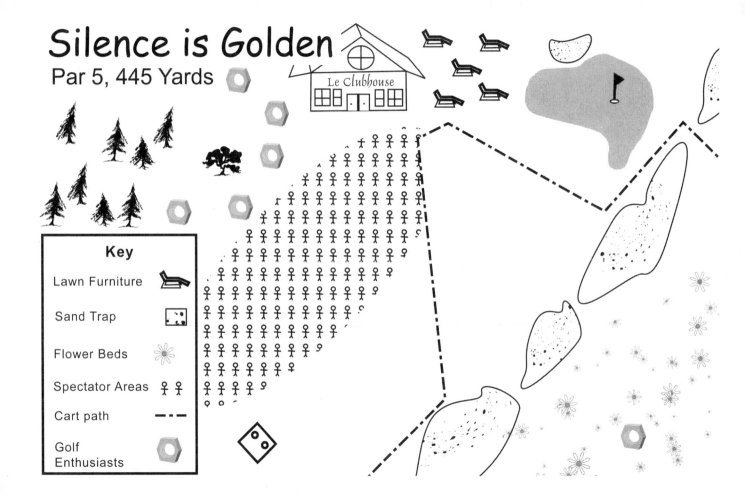

Silence is Golden
Par 5, 445 Yards

Le Clubhouse

Key

Lawn Furniture

Sand Trap

Flower Beds

Spectator Areas

Cart path

Golf Enthusiasts

This par 4 is the finishing hole at an all-inclusive family resort. It's fairly easy except for the continuous bunkers down the right side and the lightning fast green. Oh, and the fact that there is always a noisy crowd gathered around the pool next to the green.

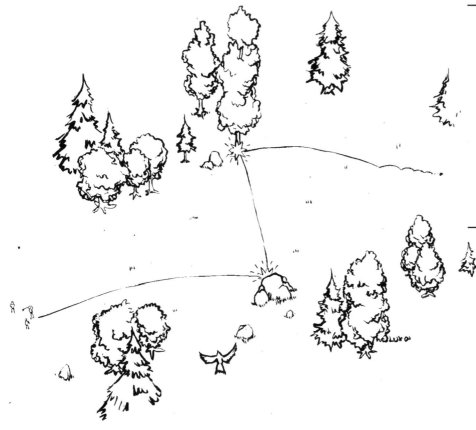

Donald steps up to the tee and swats one towards the green. It slices right, rebounds left, bounces right again and ends up in a sweet lie in the middle of the fairway.

No worries. Donald's
in great position.

Donald chips for the green, playing
to the crowd. What style and grace!

He plumb bobs the putt.

He sights the putt.

He carefully prepares to putt the ball, trying to block the crowd from consciousness.

Hey, Dudes, QUIET!
Have you no respect for
putters on the green?
Donald needs a large
helping of my next
invention!

Green Silencer

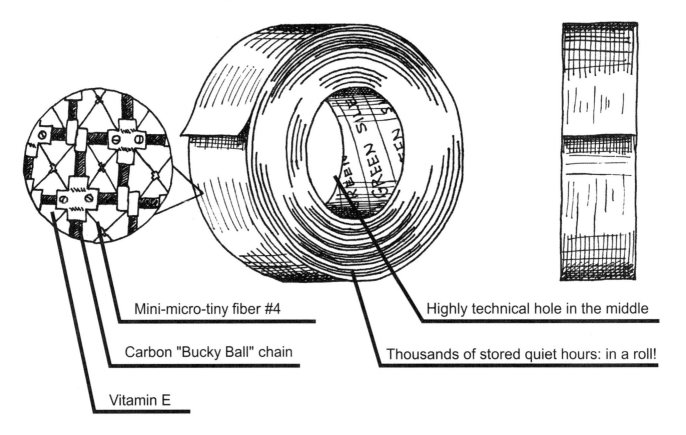

Mini-micro-tiny fiber #4

Carbon "Bucky Ball" chain

Vitamin E

Highly technical hole in the middle

Thousands of stored quiet hours: in a roll!

Imagine you are on the green in critical-putt territory. The excitement is building, but you are trying to keep your cool. Just as you are about to putt, the silence is broken by loud, insensitive people who have chosen your part of the course for a debate over swizzle sticks. You make it clear to them that they should take it somewhere else for health reasons, but they continue to disrupt your putt with their obnoxious behavior. What can you do? Green Silencer will give you the peace and serenity you need. I've conveniently designed it in roll form for maximum portability. Created with the latest molecular chain technology, it has a tensile strength of over 2,000,000,000 pounds. Capable of sticking to oily, wet, and even vodka covered surfaces, Green Silencer will stop the irritating noise and you can putt like the pros.

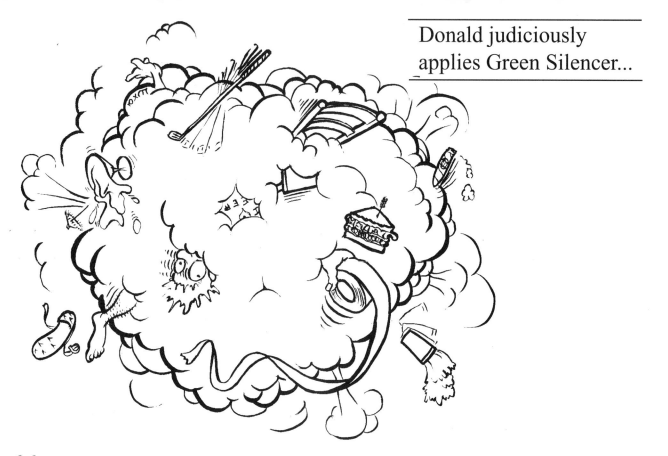

...and makes the putt
in golden silence!

Alternate uses of Green Silencer

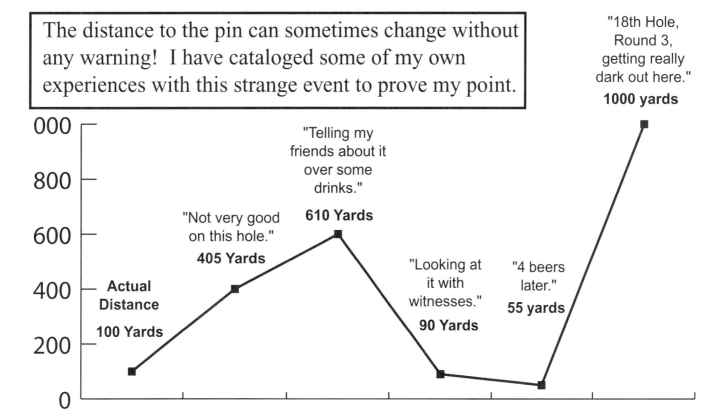

The distance to the pin can sometimes change without any warning! I have cataloged some of my own experiences with this strange event to prove my point.

"18th Hole, Round 3, getting really dark out here."
1000 yards

"Telling my friends about it over some drinks."
610 Yards

"Not very good on this hole."
405 Yards

"Looking at it with witnesses."
90 Yards

"4 beers later."
55 yards

Actual Distance
100 Yards

Hole #7

Over the Edge

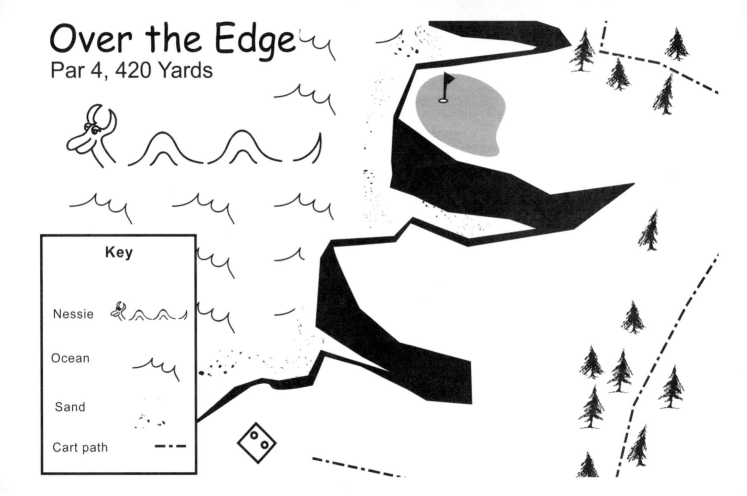

Over the Edge
Par 4, 420 Yards

Key

Nessie

Ocean

Sand

Cart path

This hole runs along the seacoast and has intervening sea cliffs projecting through the fairway. Although it is very dramatic looking, it also means that a short drive is unplayable. Many golfers simply take the easy way out; they hit short for the nearest solid ground and hope for a bogey. The real gamblers are willing to take the Big Dog out and drive over the rocks for a chance at par.

While Jake practices his interperative dance, *The Day You Missed So Bad*, Donald shoots one into the ravine.

Jake drops his club accidentally. Ohhh! Sorry, Chip. That's a nasty slice!

Nice shot! The Big Dog has bite.

A few strokes later, Chip and Donald finally catch up to the crafty Jake waiting over his ball. Seeing that their lies are similar, Jake employs a bit of deception.

Jake's second shot skids by the hole..will it hold or take a bath? He rushes to the green in case he needs to use the Golf Gadget he has carefully concealed.

Velcro Pocket

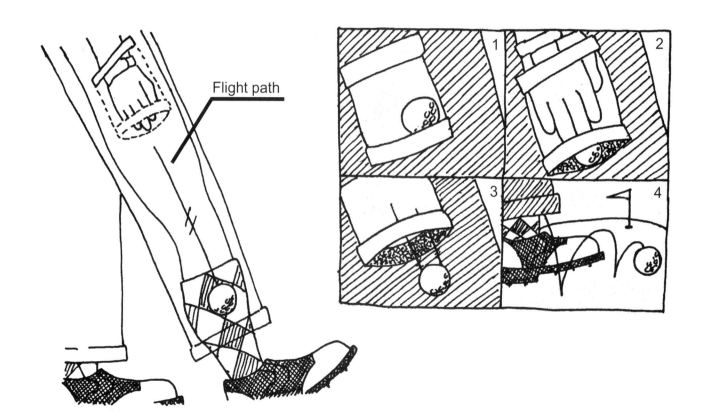

Flight path

Has your ball ever been irrevocably destroyed? Has it been lost in fathomless depths? The Velcro Pocket will save you at least one critical stroke...maybe more. Used judiciously, it may be possible to win an entire tournament with this single device. Install the invention inside the pocket of your favorite golf pants and reap the benefits of timely ball replacement.

Simply follow these steps:

1. Place a ball with your personal mark in your pocket.
2. When the ball in play is lost, hustle to the place where your opponents last saw it.
3. Put your hand in the pocket and release the ball when nobody is watching.
4. Yell, "I've got it!"

Great lie, Jake...no pun intended.

Alternate Uses for the Velcro Pocket

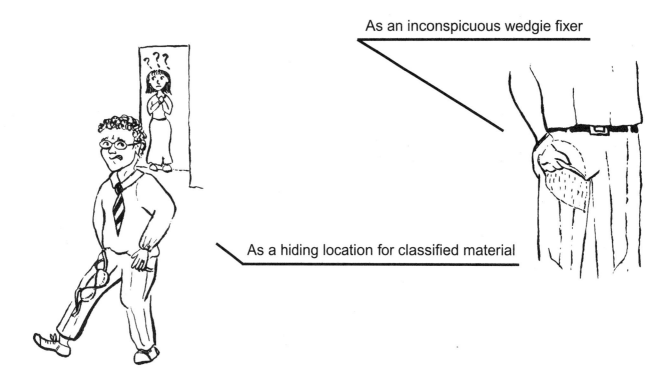

As an inconspicuous wedgie fixer

As a hiding location for classified material

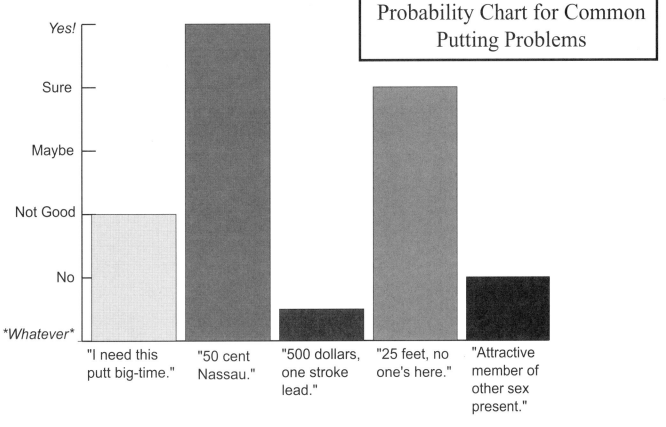

Probability Chart for Common Putting Problems

Yes!
Sure
Maybe
Not Good
No
Whatever

"I need this putt big-time."
"50 cent Nassau."
"500 dollars, one stroke lead."
"25 feet, no one's here."
"Attractive member of other sex present."

Hole #8

Avian Issues

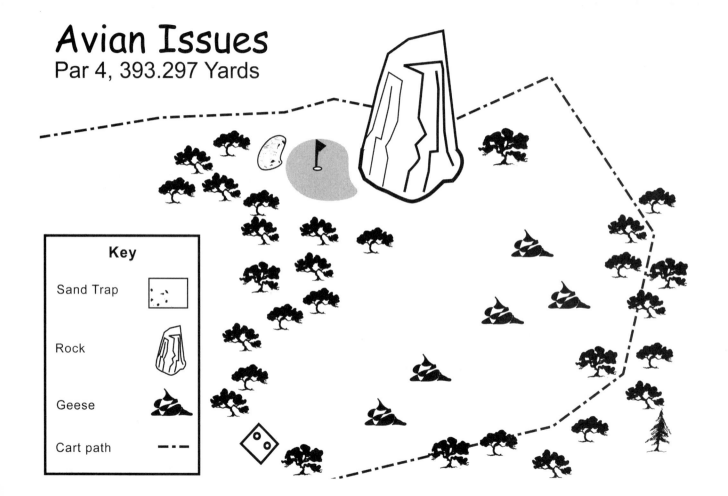

Avian Issues
Par 4, 393.297 Yards

Key

Sand Trap	
Rock	
Geese	
Cart path	- · - · -

This mountain course is dominated by a craggy rock outcropping to the right of the green. Although picturesque, this mighty stone has given many golfers plenty of extra strokes. Balls that strike it go bounding off into the wilderness, never to be seen again. However, due to a fiendish course layout, the other side of the monolith is in bounds! Players on the wrong side of the thing must play their way out and usually pile up huge numbers of strokes. The hole is all uphill, with a long gently curving fairway and a sharp left dog leg at the end. Par 4.

With Donald and Chip short in the fairway, Jake puts together a beautiful drive. On the basis of this one drive, Jake starts making his PGA Tour plans.

Stupid geese on the fairway again. Watch where you walk. Don't lick the ball!

Jake takes wildlife management into his own hands.

Arrgh! The foul birds counter-attack from behind!

Well, it looks like Jake is going to lose his shirt for sure on this one. Trapped behind this massive hunk of stone, it will take at least two more strokes to get a shot to the green. But don't count him out - he has another of my gadgets in his bag to help rescue him.

The "H" Ball

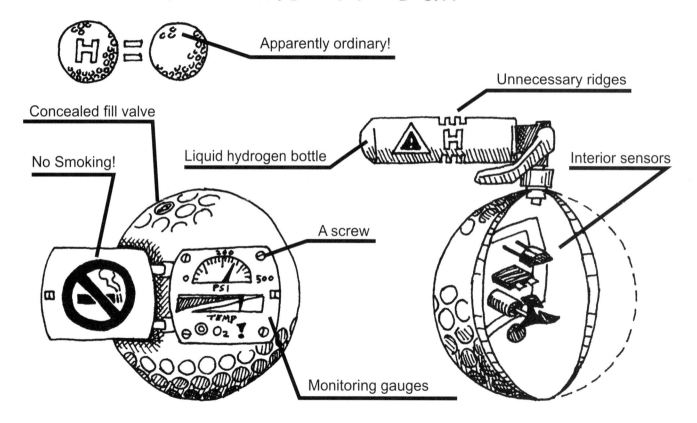

Apparently ordinary!

Unnecessary ridges

Concealed fill valve

No Smoking!

Liquid hydrogen bottle

Interior sensors

A screw

300

500

PSI

TEMP

O₂

Monitoring gauges

This invention is for all those golfers who enjoy the thrill of a perfect wedge shot. Sharp contact is followed by a graceful curve that arcs beautifully over the player's head, landing precisely on the green with just the smallest roll to carry it to the waiting cup. Ah, it is so miraculous! The arc, the hang time, the quick stop. Why not enjoy the experience a moment longer? Enter the H Ball! This ball takes advantage of pure hydrogen to greatly increase loft. Because hydrogen has a couple of other attributes, a few additions to the traditional golf ball were necessary to reduce the incidence of in-flight fires. Warning: No smoking is advised when using this invention.

Jake substitutes the H Ball and gives it a new charge.

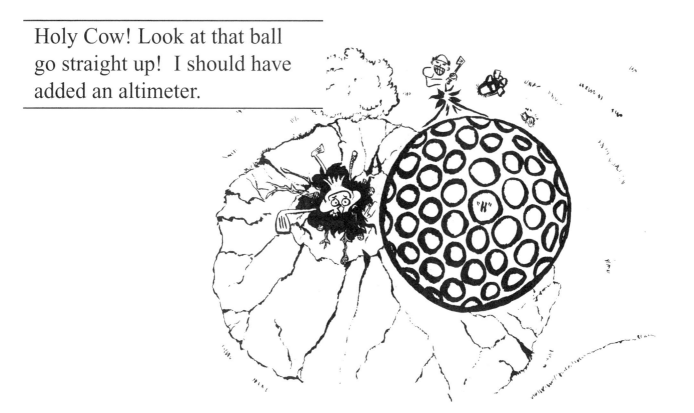

Holy Cow! Look at that ball go straight up! I should have added an altimeter.

Victory to the H Ball! The other guys can't believe what hit them!

Alternate Uses for the H Ball

H Ball as a hand-held, anti-personnel device.

The H Ball as a gas grill fuel unit.

Hole #9

A Friendly Wager

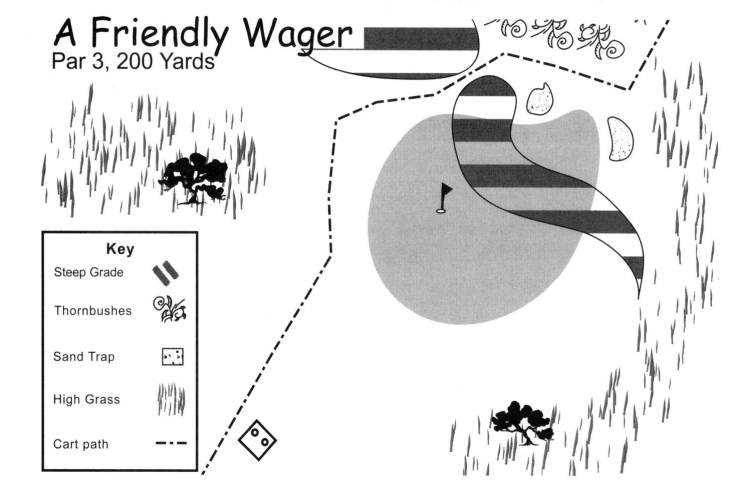

A Friendly Wager
Par 3, 200 Yards

Key

Steep Grade

Thornbushes

Sand Trap

High Grass

Cart path

Par 3, 200 yards. This is not a hard hole since the tee is elevated and the wind is generally coming from your back. The green is very tough to putt, though, so three putts are common.

Jake talks Chip into a little
side bet. It's only 1000
shares of stock - once worth
thousands, now about the
same as one roll of TP.

Both Chip and Jake are safely on the green. Donald is so far OB that he's decided to have another beer and sit this hole out.

Jake's putt has a little right-to-left break...

...but he sinks his second putt for par.

TAP!

Chip's putt is a little downhill.

What an amazing putt! Chip is within a foot of the hole. Without another of my brilliant gadgets, the hole will be tied and no market shares will be traded today.

Yip-Inducing Socks

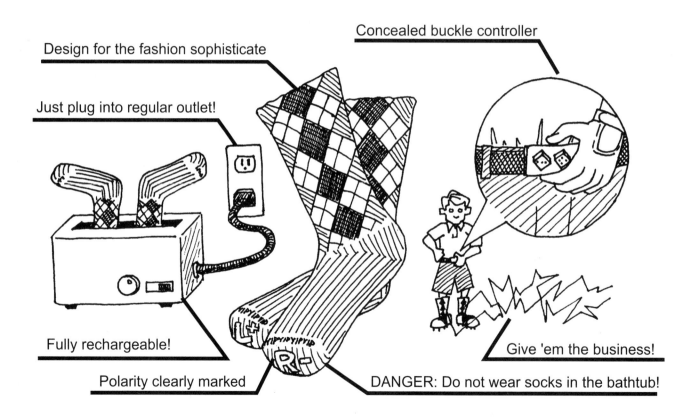

Design for the fashion sophisticate

Just plug into regular outlet!

Concealed buckle controller

Fully rechargeable!

Polarity clearly marked

Give 'em the business!

DANGER: Do not wear socks in the bathtub!

Are your opponents counting on superior skill to beat you on the greens? Well, let me tell you, they won't get away with it for long after they've had a dose of my Yip-Inducing Socks. This invention is capable of distracting the victim, er, opponent indefinitely. These twin devices are designed to deliver 1000 volts each for a heck of a jolt! They have a maximum range of twelve feet, are fully rechargeable, and deliver their wallop so quickly the wearer does not fall under suspicion. The remote trigger is concealed behind your favorite belt buckle. I have discovered that traditional argyle colors are the most effective as they naturally induce disorientation and nausea. If both socks are used, one at a time, at different holes, I guarantee the victim will develop a genuine case of the yips at most greens!

Chip misses the tap-in and gets a bogie.

Jake wins the bet and all the stock.

Alternate Uses for Yip-Inducing Socks

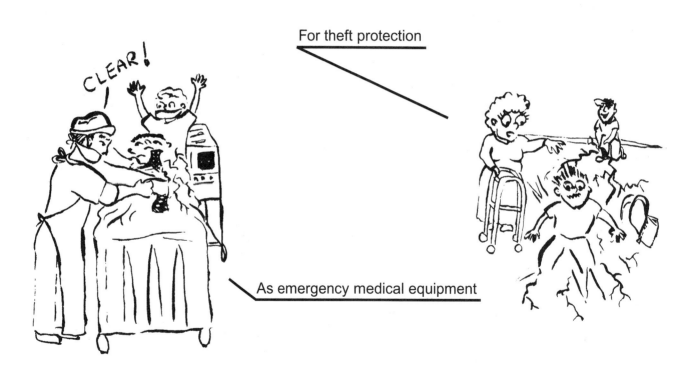

For theft protection

As emergency medical equipment

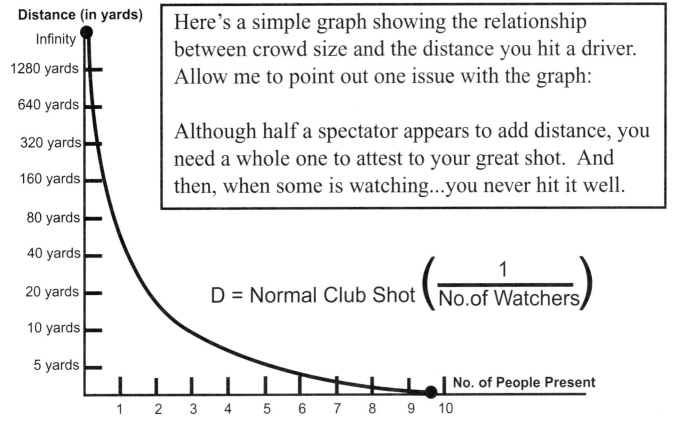

Distance (in yards)

Infinity	
1280 yards	
640 yards	
320 yards	
160 yards	
80 yards	
40 yards	
20 yards	
10 yards	
5 yards	

No. of People Present

1   2   3   4   5   6   7   8   9   10

Here's a simple graph showing the relationship between crowd size and the distance you hit a driver. Allow me to point out one issue with the graph:

Although half a spectator appears to add distance, you need a whole one to attest to your great shot. And then, when some is watching...you never hit it well.

$$D = \text{Normal Club Shot} \left(\frac{1}{\text{No. of Watchers}} \right)$$

As we have seen, technology can do the world of golf a world of good. But do the rules makers listen to my cause? No! They drone on and on about the benefits of practice and lessons - like those are going to help *your* game *this* afternoon! Fortunately, we now have my Golf Gadgets. They lowered my friends' scores and they will have you shooting even par in no time. In the meantime, I will continue to work on new weapons for our arsenal. The next round of Gadgets is coming soon. However there are a few bugs, ah, features that need work. Here's a preview.

The Rocket Roller

This ball was designed with extra ground roll in mind. When struck by a club, the ball's onboard trigger is set. When it next strikes the ground, it takes off like a rocket! It would be excellent for going under trees and up wooded inclines, if I could just keep it from setting fire to the grounds! You wouldn't believe the size of the ruts fire trucks make in a wet fairway...I have some further development to do on this.

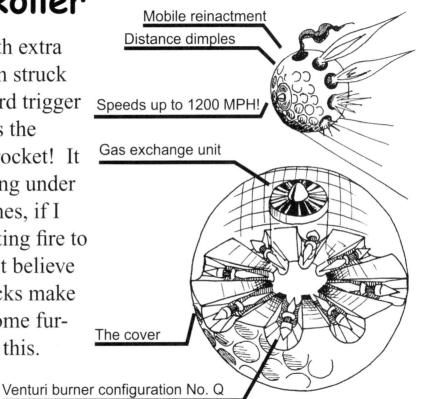

Mobile reinactment

Distance dimples

Speeds up to 1200 MPH!

Gas exchange unit

The cover

Venturi burner configuration No. Q

Cart Super Charger

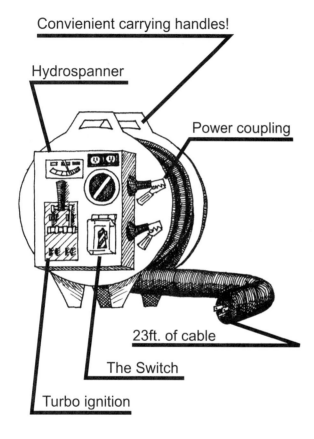

Convienient carrying handles!

Hydrospanner

Power coupling

23ft. of cable

The Switch

Turbo ignition

What really annoys the average golfer? Poor golf cart performance - that's why I've invented the Cart Super Charger! The Charger is capable of propelling any ordinary cart up to 122 MPH! It's unique fission engine utilizes relatively cheap Russian nuclear fuel rods that would normally just be bought up by bad guys. When the rod is spent, flush the Charger with warm water into your sink at home, and remember to recycle the metal rod along with your aluminum cans...er...maybe not...I'll work on this.

Self-Adjusting Marker

Just because your ball stops in a crummy spot doesn't mean you have to play it there. Not with my Self-Adjusting Marker! It will leap closer to the pin on its own, and if I can get it to stop jumping, it will be fairly stealthy as well! I'll work on that, too.

Powerful spring!

Aerodynamic shape

Ordinary looking surface

A compass rose for marker orientation

The Self-Adjusting Marker in action!

The End
(for now...)

I am an inventor and strive to solve all of golf's dilemmas by designing special gadgets. I am preparing my next round of golf gadgets to reduce your score a few more strokes. If you have any golf problems requiring a solution, devices to be engineered, or golf situations for which you need an escape, feel free to e-mail me at gbrobst@gebcoeng.com. Device or scenario descriptions become the property of Sonoma Publishers. You can't take a tax deduction for the contribution, but you will get your name in print.

-BRANDO

Sketch Pad for Gadget Submission

Sketch Pad for Gadget Submission

Sketch Pad for Gadget Submission